A Monster on the Street

Part 1

written by Jeremy Strong
illustrated by Steve Smallman

Chapter One

The Queen of Sheba

Sam had some news for her friends. "There's a removal van outside the house with the SOLD sign," she said. "New people are moving in."

"I wonder what they're like," said Mouse.

The children went out to look,
but they could not see the new people.

"Nothing's happening," said Ben. "Let's go
to the secret room."

The friends went to their secret room and sat on the floor. Jojo opened the tin and passed the biscuits round. Sam didn't want one.

"Aren't you hungry?" asked Ben.

Sam shook her head.

"But you love biscuits," laughed Jojo.

"You must be ill!"

Sam didn't smile.

"Mum and Dad have had another argument," she told her friends. "I was in bed. I could hear them shouting at each other."

"My parents argue sometimes," said Ben. "What was it about?"
"Dad keeps working nights at the Fire Station so Mum never gets to see him. Things like that."

Sam let out a long sigh and gazed round the
secret room. "The flat feels horrible. I wish I
could live here."

The other children were silent. They did not
know what to say. Sam was normally so
bubbly.

Jojo wanted to cheer Sam up. "Come on.
Let's watch the new people move in."

The friends scrambled out from beneath the bushes. As they got to their feet they almost fell over a boy and girl they had never seen before.

The boy had short, spiky hair,

ears
that
stuck
out,

and a big, cheeky grin.

But it was the boy's little sister that made
their eyes boggle.

She looked about six.

Wild, dark hair
exploded from her head like a firework.

She was wearing strange clothes. She
had her mum's beads around her neck.
Her skinny arms were covered with bangles.

"Hello!" said the new boy, with a big smile.
"I'm Duncan Hart." He put a hand on his
sister's shoulder and pushed her forward.
"And this is the Queen of Sheba."

Chapter Two

The Monster Escapes

The Queen of Sheba stretched out one arm.
Most of the bangles slid down and fell off.
"You may kiss my hand,"
said the
little Queen.
She suddenly
smiled at Jojo.
"Can we
come to tea
at your house?"
she asked.
Duncan
groaned.

Before the twins could answer Duncan explained. "Our mum's a terrible cook."

"She's trying to poison us!" said the
Queen of Sheba, with big round eyes.
"She's not really," said Duncan.
"That's what you said, Duncan Donut,"
cried the Queen.
"It was a joke," Duncan explained.

"Duncan Donut?" Ben said.

"That's what my friends call me," Duncan explained.

"And my sister is not really the Queen of Sheba. Her proper name is Cleopatra."

Donut

The Queen of Sheba

"But Cleopatra was the Queen of Egypt, not the Queen of Sheba," Ben pointed out.

"I know," said Donut, "but when Cleo got up this morning she insisted on being the Queen of Sheba. If we don't agree she stamps her feet!"

"No I don't!" cried Cleo, stamping her mum's high heeled shoes.

Donut sighed again. "See what I mean?" Sam smiled at last.

Sam looked up at Donut. "We were going to watch the removal van unload."

"That's our van," said Donut. "Dad sent us out to explore. He said we were getting under his feet."

"He's not our real dad," Cleo butted in. "He's just pretend."

Donut laughed. "She means he's our step-dad. Mum got married again."

A man came out of
the van carrying a
large bird cage.
There was a
beautiful parrot inside.

The bird opened
his big beak and
stuck out a thick,
grey tongue.

"He's called Icarus,"
said Cleo proudly,
and she stuck out her
tongue at Icarus.

The removal men begun to unload a strange black monster.

"What's that?" asked Mouse.

"Mum's grand piano," Donut said. "She plays the piano and Dad sings. When he does, it's so bad we have to hide."

The men struggled to get the heavy piano down the ramp.

"Hold on there," puffed one man.

"I'm losing my grip!" warned another.

"It's getting away! **Watch out!**" yelled a third man.

There was a
dreadful rumble
as the big piano escaped
from the men and slid down
the ramp. The man at the front
had to jump on top so that he didn't
get run over by the three-legged monster.

Moments later the wild,
black beast was heading off
down the road, faster and faster.
The man clung to the top of the piano.

The children watched with horror.
What could they do?

Find out what happens in A Monster on the Street Part 2.